Punctuation Matters
Book 2

G000167900

It is intended that this book should be used to reinforce key skills as recommended in the English National Curriculum at Key Stage 2 and in the National Literacy Strategy.

CONTENTS

by Hilda King

Hilda King Educational, Ashwells Manor Drive, Penn, Buckinghamshire HP10 8EU

Typeset by: Penn Secretarial Services
Illustrations by: Brian Watson
Printed by: Watkiss Studios

First Published 1998
Reprinted 1999
Reprinted 2001
Reprinted 2002

ISBN 1 873533 52 7

> **Remember:**
> the most common use of the comma is to separate different parts of a sentence. Where there is a natural pause, a comma makes the meaning of a sentence clearer.
> e.g. I can dive, swim two lengths and float.
> N.B. You do not usually need a comma before or after the word 'and'.

Rewrite the sentences below and add the commas.

1. When I try to sharpen a pencil the lead always breaks.

....

2. He jumped over the box climbed the wall bars and reached the top.

....

3. She typed the letter signed it but forgot to post it.

....

4. I like to get up early have breakfast and then brush my teeth.

....

5. I went to Los Angeles San Francisco and San Diego.

....

6. If you go to the sales early you should find some bargains.

....

7. Tomorrow instead of having lessons we are going on a school trip.

....

8. Whenever it rains I forget my umbrella.

....

9. My sister who is ten will run in a marathon race.

....

10. The ducklings although very small could swim.

....

The comma

> **Remember:**
> commas are used to separate items on a list.
> e.g. I ate cakes, jelly, sandwiches and sausages.

Rewrite the sentences below and add the commas.

1. I went to the shops and bought apples oranges and grapes.

....

2. We took the car to have the tyres the water and the oil checked.

....

3. My house has a lounge kitchen bathroom and two bedrooms.

....

4. You can skip hop or jump.

....

5. Do not forget your ruler pencil rubber or pen.

....

6. I can run quickly slowly sideways or backwards.

....

> **Remember:**
> a comma can change the meaning of a sentence.
> e.g.   I met Peter, James and John.
>   I met Peter James and John.

Rewrite the sentences below, add the commas to alter the meaning.

1. Gemma is a pretty intelligent girl.

....

2. My uncle George and Ayesha came to meet me.

....

3. I saw Philip Martin and Nathan at the party.

....

The comma

> **Remember:**
> a comma is used when adding a name.
> e.g. The driver, Mr. Walker, is tall.

Rewrite the sentences below and add the commas.

1. I saw the two large dogs Bouncer and George chasing the cat.

....

2. Miss Jones one of my teachers has a loud voice.

....

3. Beethoven one of the greatest composers was born in Germany.

....

4. Mr Edwards our next-door neighbour has three pet rats.

....

5. The famous painting the Mona Lisa is very beautiful.

....

6. The film about an otter Ring of Bright Water is very sad.

....

> **Remember:**
> a comma helps to make a meaning clearer.
> e.g. It is time to eat, Mary.

Rewrite the sentences below and add the commas.

1. We went to hear a group play Susan.

....

2. Did you know Patrick Jean?

....

3. I went to feed Bilbo the sea lion Liam.

....

5

The comma

> **Remember:**
> a comma is used when adding a description.
> e.g. Lucy, a fluffy, gentle cat, likes crisps.

Rewrite the sentences below and add the commas.

1. Janice a tall pretty girl won the race.

   ....

2. The River Trent a large river in England is very wide in parts.

   ....

3. The clown a funny fat man had a white face and a red nose.

   ....

4. The match watched by twenty thousand people took place at Wembley.

   ....

5. Julius Caesar a powerful Roman leader conquered England.

   ....

6. The prince a young and handsome man married a duchess.

   ....

7. The lion a bold and proud animal is known as the king of beasts.

   ....

8. The cave being so deep and narrow was dangerous for potholers.

   ....

9. The bride's dress handmade of pure silk looked lovely.

   ....

10. The apple tree although very old always has juicy apples.

    ....

11. A Christmas Carol a famous book by Charles Dickens has been made
    into a film.

    ....

    ....

The comma

Rewrite the sentences below and add the commas.

1. The walk so I am told takes two hours.

....

2. The bus by the way is always late.

....

3. Australia as we all know was discovered by Captain Cook.

....

4. The lions in the park can I believe be very dangerous.

....

5. You will of course win a prize.

....

6. Saturday I always feel is a good day for shopping.

....

7. Whatever happens do not cross the road until it is safe.

....

8. I am sure that no matter how long it takes she will finish it.

....

9. She is a good cook I think but she uses too much salt.

....

10. The Hobbit although very long is an exciting book.

....

11. Zahid in spite of my warning jumped into the pool.

....

The comma

Put in the commas in the sentences below.
Write the sentences leaving out the words enclosed in the commas.

1. I shall if I save my pocket money be able to go shopping with my friend.

    ....

2. The man who was very strong carried the huge rock.

    ....

3. We climbed the hill even though we were tired and reached the top.

    ....

4. The butterfly so colourful and small landed on the flower.

    ....

5. She like her father is good at sport.

    ....

6. The squirrel having collected the acorns ran up the tree.

    ....

7. An American athlete who ran very fast won the race.

    ....

8. The clock which belonged to my aunt keeps good time.

    ....

9. The dog who was called Charlie chased the ball.

    ....

10. The water though cold was very refreshing.

    ....

11. The red shoes which fitted well matched my new dress.

    ....

The comma

Revision page

Rewrite the sentences below and add the commas.

1. The mountain bicycle which I bought from my friend works very well.

....

2. I took my trainers racquet track suit and towel with me.

....

3. Her hat covered in feathers stopped me from seeing the screen.

....

4. Ann Hazel Catherine and Jane are in our group.

....

5. The maple tree with the sun shining on its red leaves is very pretty.

....

6. If you go the wrong way you will end up in a field.

....

7. Mr. Benson the old caretaker works very hard.

....

8. In our garden there are roses daffodils tulips and pansies.

....

9. The artist who is my uncle sketches very well.

....

10. I shall I hope dive off the top board today.

....

Complete the sentences below and add commas where needed.

1. Mrs. Lock .... is very strict.

2. I went to the supermarket and bought nine .... a cake five
   .... one kilo of .... and some lemonade.

3. I was allowed to go skating even though ....
   and I had not finished my essay.

4. Eggs flour and milk ....to make a batter
   for pancakes.

9

The exclamation mark

> An exclamation mark is used to express shock,
> surprise, delight or anger.
> e.g. Help!

Add the exclamation marks or full stops.

1. Beware

2. I've won first prize

3. I'm drowning Help

4. Come quickly The house is on fire

5. Be quiet Dad is listening to the football results

6. Goodness He's coming back in five minutes

7. What a dreadful film Shall we go home and watch a video?

8. Don't panic They've put out the fire

Make up sentences which need exclamation marks.

....

....

....

....

Add the question marks, exclamation marks or full stops.

1. Sit still I am trying to cut your toenails

2. Listen Can you hear the thunder

3. Have you seen the Loch Ness Monster Of course not

4. Quick The bus is leaving

5. Can you go to camp Gosh No

6. It is very late Why are you still awake

7. Goodness Have you seen the state of the carpet

8. Quick The cat's been sick

10

The exclamation mark

An exclamation mark can be used for special effect or emphasis.
e.g. Come here! Your homework is in a mess!
Come here! I have a cake for you.

In each set of examples, one line needs one or two exclamation marks and the other needs full stops. Add the correct punctuation.

1. My watch is wrong I must get it mended

    My watch is wrong I'm late

2. The Queen has arrived Stand up

    The Queen has arrived She looks very well

3. Please help me I am looking for my hamster

    Please help My hamster has escaped

4. Stop The traffic light is red

    Please stop here I want to go to the bank

5. Take this tray quickly It's too heavy

    Take this tray There are some sandwiches on it for you

6. You can move the ladder now The paint is dry

    Move The ladder is falling

7. Watch out The boat is sinking

    Watch out for the boat It is coming into harbour

8. Wait for me please My sandal is undone

    Wait My foot is bleeding

9. We will never get tickets Just look at the queue

    We were lucky to get tickets The queue was very long

The apostrophe

> **An apostrophe is used to show that a letter or letters are missed out.**
>
> e.g. I am hot.   I'm hot.
>
> The apostrophe takes the place of the a.

Write the examples below in full without the apostrophes.

Note: only *one* letter has been left out.

I'm	....	....	wasn't	....	....
you're	....	....	didn't	....	....
he's	....	....	couldn't	....	....
she's	....	....	wouldn't	....	....
* it's	....	....	shouldn't	....	....
we're	....	....	haven't	....	....
they're	....	....	doesn't	....	....
isn't	....	....	hasn't	....	....
aren't	....	....	that's	....	....
weren't	....	....	what's	....	....

Make the examples below into one word by using an apostrophe.

did not	....	how is	....
here is	....	were not	....
there is	....	you are	....
where is	....	who is	....
have not	....	are not	....

In the examples below change *two* words into *one* by adding an apostrophe. Write the word at the side.

He has not seen the full moon.   ....

Here is the book that was missing.   ....

They could not practise their spellings.   ....

Write some sentences on a piece of paper using the apostrophe in this way.

* See page 16 for detailed explanation of the use of its and it's.

The apostrophe

Sometimes an apostrophe takes the place of more than one letter.

e.g. I cannot see him.   I can't see him.

n and **o** are replaced with an **apostrophe**.

In the examples below change one word into two by leaving out the apostrophes. Write the extra letters at the side.

I'll	....I.....	.shall..	<u>s</u> <u>h</u> <u>a</u>	they'll	....	....	_ _
you'll	....	....	_ _	I've	....	....	_ _
he'll	....	....	_ _	you've	....	....	_ _
she'll	....	....	_ _	we've	....	....	_ _
it'll	....	....	_ _	they've	....	....	_ _
we'll	....	....	_ _ _	who've	....	....	_ _

Remember:
he's is short for **he is**, or **he has**.

he was is *never* shortened e.g. He **was** last.

In the examples below change *two* words into *one* by adding an apostrophe. <u>Underline</u> the two words then write the apostrophe word at the side.

1. I know that he will like his present.   ....

2. I shall see you next week.   ....

3. He will take the exam tomorrow.   ....

4. We have been for a long walk.   ....

5. Can you tell me if they have had tea?   ....

6. It will be all right on the night.   ....

7. If you try hard you will succeed.   ....

8. The people who have won the prizes are very pleased.   ....

9. Are you sure you have had enough to eat?   ....

The apostrophe

| More words where an apostrophe is used. |

In the examples below change **one** word into **two** by leaving out the apostrophe. Remember: they are **all** in the present tense.

they're   ....   we're   ....

you're   ....

> **Remember: they were, we were, you were, I was, he was and she was are always written in *full*.**

Rewrite the sentences below using apostrophes where possible.

1.   Hurry up! They are coming soon.

....

2.   We knew that we were right and he was wrong.

....

3.   He says we are early but we are not.

....

4.   I think you are good at sport.

....

5.   She was looking forward to her piano lesson.

....

6.   He is moving to a new house.

....

7.   They are very good value for money.

....

8.   We look alike because we are sisters.

....

9.   We were going shopping to buy some books.

....

The apostrophe

Sometimes the apostrophe takes the place of four or five letters.
e.g. He would rather go now.   He'd rather go now.
The apostrophe takes the place of the letters **woul.**

Make these examples into one word by using the apostrophes.

I should   ....   he would   ....

you would   ....   we should   ....

she would   ....   they would   ....

N.B. o'clock is always used for **of the clock.**

Rewrite the sentences below using apostrophes where possible.

1. He said that they would never agree.

....

2.   You would be frightened if you stepped on a snake.

....

3.   They told us that we should be able to sit at the front.

....

4.   She said that she would go to see the film.

....

5.   It should not be dangerous and it will be fun.

....

6.   My dad could not go until six of the clock.

....

Occasionally, a letter is added and then the word abbreviated with an apostrophe. e.g. will not - won't

Rewrite the sentences using apostrophes where possible.

1.   She will not go in the attic because she has seen a mouse there.

....

2.   They will not go near because of the alligators in the lake.

....

The apostrophe

> ### its and it's
>
> **its** shows that something belongs to it. e.g. The dog bit **its** own tail.
>
> **it's** means it is. e.g. **It's** a lovely day today.
>
> **it's** means it has e.g. **It's** been very wet this week.

its or it's?

Write the right words in the spaces.

1. The school had ………. Christmas party yesterday.
2. I think ………. time to play tennis.
3. The monkey sat in ………. own dinner.
4. I hope ………. not too busy.
5. Isa says that ………. always hot in India.
6. The Air Force flew ………. first jet plane.

its or it's?

In the following sentences, two words are in the wrong place.
Rewrite each sentence as it should be written.

1. The its chased tiger prey.

....

2. I think snow going to it's.

....

3. The adder is dangerous; poisonous venom is its.

....

4. The newspaper changed name its.

....

5. They say that skate hard to it's.

....

6. I think that go fun to it's to Stoke Park.

....

Write a sentence using **its** and **it's** in it.

....

The apostrophe

Revision page

Space out the words and put in the apostrophes.
The first one is done for you.

1.   Ithinkitsfun.   I think it's fun.

2.   HesgoingtoAfrica.   ....

3.   Shehasnthadherhaircut.   ....

4.   Whatsonthetelevision?   ....

5.   Itsagoodbook.   ....

6.   Hedoesntmind.   ....

7.   Wheresmybag?   ....

8.   Werenotgoingtothefair.   ....

9.   Shesateacher.   ....

10. Thatsagoodidea.   ....

Letters are sometimes missed out between a noun and a verb.
e.g. The computer's broken.   **The computer is broken.**
e.g. The computer's broken down.   **The computer has broken down.**

Rewrite the sentences below replacing the apostrophes with the
missing letters.

1.   My friend's sad. He's lost his pen   ....

2.   The hat's too big.   ....

3.   He hasn't chosen me to play in the team.

....

4.   They aren't happy to go if it's busy.

....

5.   Who's going to see if he's all right?

....

6.   We're not sure if he's won the cup.

....

7.   Where's the mouse? The cage's empty.

....

The belonging apostrophe

> **The apostrophe has another use.**
> **It is used with s at the end of a noun.**
> **It shows that something or someone belongs to that noun.**

e.g. the **dog's** tail   the tail **of the dog**
e.g. my **friend's** sister   the sister **of my friend**
e.g. the **teacher's** voice   the voice **of the teacher**

Put the apostrophes into the examples below.

1. the horses head
2. the sharks fin
3. the cats owner
4. the lorrys tyres
5. the babys rattle
6. Williams uncle
7. my dads job
8. the teams mascot
9. Jennys bag
10. the swimming pools edge
11. the girls dress
12. the rats tail
13. the dogs dinner
14. the boys cricket bat

Make up four examples of your own.

....

....

Put the apostrophes in the sentences below.

1. The taps washer was worn.
2. It is Janes birthday next week.
3. Do you know if that is Stephens photograph?
4. Can you find your mothers purse?
5. Ranjits bike is very smart.
6. I hope the dogs bark will not wake the neighbours baby.

18

The belonging apostrophe

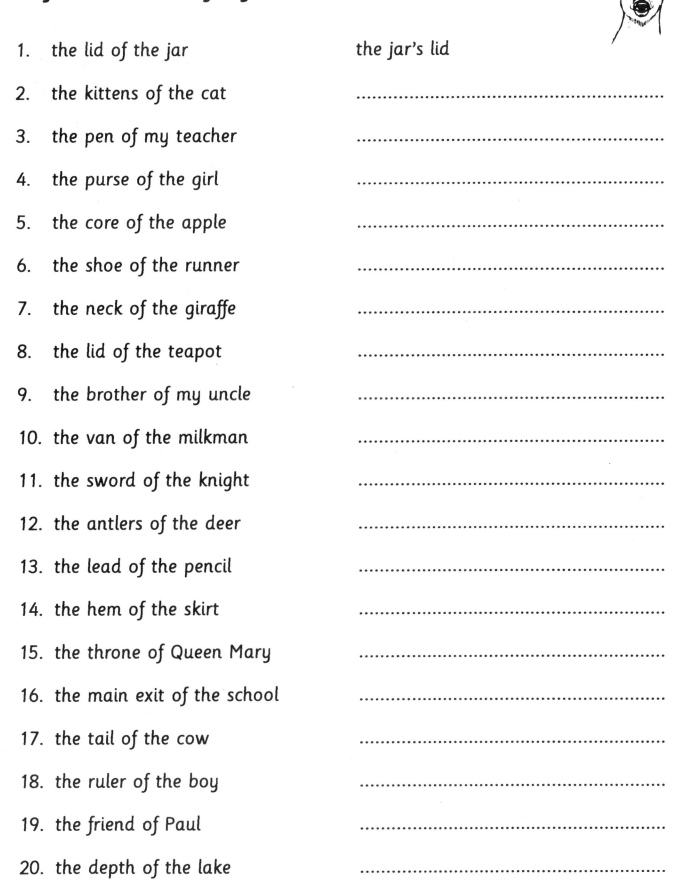

Rewrite the examples below using the belonging apostrophe.
The first one is done for you.

1. the lid of the jar   the jar's lid

2. the kittens of the cat   ....

3. the pen of my teacher ....

4. the purse of the girl   ....

5. the core of the apple   ....

6. the shoe of the runner ....

7. the neck of the giraffe ....

8. the lid of the teapot   ....

9. the brother of my uncle ....

10. the van of the milkman ....

11. the sword of the knight ....

12. the antlers of the deer ....

13. the lead of the pencil ....

14. the hem of the skirt   ....

15. the throne of Queen Mary ....

16. the main exit of the school ....

17. the tail of the cow   ....

18. the ruler of the boy   ....

19. the friend of Paul   ....

20. the depth of the lake ....

The belonging apostrophe

> **If a singular word already ends in s add 's.**
>
> **e.g. the boss's car   e.g. Ross's house**

*A FAMILY TREE

```
                    David  m  Phyllis
                          |
    ┌──────────────┬──────────────┬──────────────┐
Marcus m Jess    Paul      John m Clare      Mavis m Tom
    |                          |                    |
 ┌──┬──┐                    ┌──┴──┐                 |
Bob Beth Simon           Morris  Adam            Iris
```

Look at the family tree above.

Answer the questions below. Use the belonging apostrophes in your answers. The first one is done for you.

1. Who is the wife of David?   David's wife is Phyllis.

2. Who is the husband of Phyllis?   ....

3. Who is the sister of Marcus?   ....

4. Who is the daughter of Tom?   ....

5. Who is the grandmother of Adam?

....

6. Who is the father of Morris?   ....

7. Who is the daughter of Jess?   ....

8. Who is the mother of Simon?   ....

9. Who are the granddaughters of David?

....

* This may have to be explained.

The belonging apostrophe

Underline the correct example.

1. That chair's leg is broken.	That chairs' leg is broken.
2. This is Mark's scarf.	This is Marks' scarf.
3. Where is the dogs' lead?	Where is the dog's lead?
4. That is Joans' favourite song.	That is Joan's favourite song.
5. Anisa is Hassam's sister.	Anisa is Hassams' sister.

Add the apostrophe where needed.

Not all the examples will need apostrophes.

1. That is Jeans bicycle.

2. Oxfam needs lots of blankets, warm clothes and jumpers.

3. The postmans bag was full of letters.

4. There were books and toys for sale at the bazaar.

5. Jamess video tape was brilliant.

6. Peters watch was being mended so he used Rosss.

7. The plays ending was very good.

8. Mums scales were broken so she used my sisters scales.

9. We used sticky tape to hold the pages together.

10. She met me at my uncles house.

Write some sentences of your own using the belonging apostrophe.

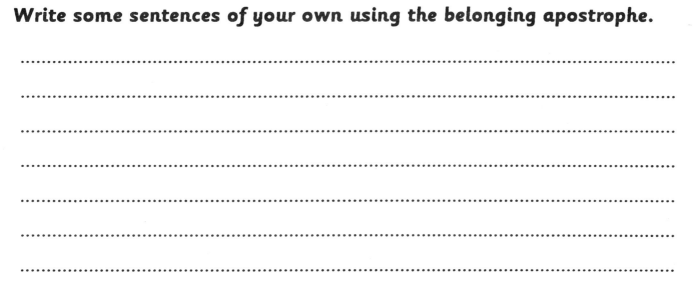

The belonging apostrophe

> **When a noun is plural and ends in s, es or ies, add an apostrophe after the s, but do not add another s.**

Singular	Plural
e.g. a **girl's** shoes	**girls'** shoes
e.g. a **doctor's** meeting	**doctors'** meeting

Singular or plural?

Write **sing** for **singular** or **pl** for **plural** at the side of each example.

1. the boys' changing rooms ....
2. a snake's skin ....
3. ladies' handbags ....
4. butterflies' wings ....
5. the car's engine ....

Make up two singular and two plural examples of your own.

....

....

Add the apostrophes in the sentences below.

1. The butchers shop is closed.
2. That is next years calendar.
3. There are birds nests in the beech trees.
4. Sandra dropped the speckled hens egg.
5. This ships sails are red.
6. My skis clip is broken.
7. Shahabs pencils were blunt.
8. The cricket teams score was high.
9 Those are Emilys shoes.

Write some sentences on a piece of paper using the **belonging apostrophe** in the same way.

22

The belonging apostrophe

> **Some plurals do not end in s.**
> **e.g. men, children**

If a plural noun does not end in **s** then add **'s** to show belonging.

e.g. the **men's** ties

e.g. the **children's** toys

Add the apostrophes to the sentences below.

1. Policemens wives can be very lonely.
2. The womens changing rooms are cold.
3. He was a wolf in sheeps clothing.
4. The mens room is on the top floor.
5. It is difficult to see trouts eyes.
6. Childrens shoes are very expensive.
7. Peoples wishes must be carried out.

Wrong words

Two words, the apostrophe word, followed by a noun have been put in the wrong sentences. Rewrite the sentences to make sense.

1. Women's shoes often clings to fences.

    ....

2. The style of sheep's wool is always changing.

    ....

3. Children's teacher are often red.

    ....

4. The postmen's bicycles always has an apple for lunch.

    ....

23

The belonging apostrophe

Revision page

Add the apostrophes to the sentences below.

1. Williams coat is too big.
2. Both the teams captains were popular.
3. The firemens hoses were tangled.
4. Somebodys watch has a loud alarm.
5. It was Nigels fault.
6. Rajs bicycle has six gears.
7. It is hard to find bears dens.
8. I clung to the horses mane.
9. I can't remember the songs name.
10. All the chains links were strong and held the ships anchor firmly.

Space out the words and put in the apostrophes.

1. Harrysparrotisveryclever.

....

2. IsawLukesteamwin.

....

3. Inearlyfelloverthecliffsedge.

....

4. Jacksbrotherisgoodatmaths.

....

5. Thethievescarbrokedown.

....

6. Iwenttotheladieshairdresser.

....

7. Thatrulersnumbersarehardtosee.

....

8. Aeroplanescargoesarekeptinthehold.

....

Common mistakes with apostrophes

Remember:

never use an apostrophe to make words plural

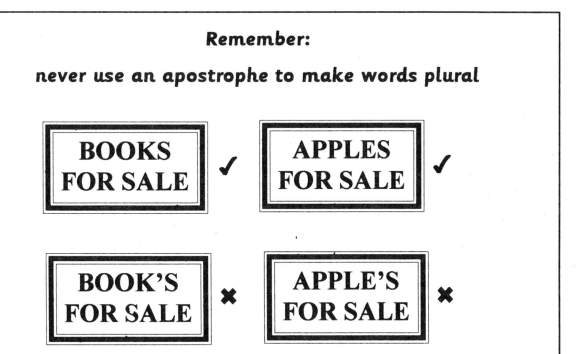

Remember:

if you are not sure where to put the apostrophe, ask yourself the following questions:

Does it **belong** to someone or something?
If so put the apostrophe **before the s.**

Is it **its** or **it's**?
If you can say **it is** then always use an **apostrophe.**

Remember:

Hers means belonging to her.   **Ours** mean belonging to us.
Yours means belonging to you.   **Theirs** means belonging to them.

There is **no** apostrophe before the **s.**

e.g. The green pencil is **hers**, the red one is **ours**, the blue pencil is
yours and the black one is **theirs**.

The apostrophes
Revision page

The apostrophe that shows letters missed out

Add the apostrophes to the sentences below.

1. Wheres my drink?
2. Its hard to understand.
3. I cant think straight.
4. I havent cleaned my teeth.
5. We arent lucky.
6. Davids gone home.

The belonging apostrophe

Add the apostrophes to the sentences below.

1. The nurses uniform was white.
2. Flamingoes legs are very thin.
3. The conjurors trick was very clever.
4. Kates photograph made us laugh.
5. The two boys diving belts were heavy.

Look at the sentences below.

<u>Underline</u> the apostrophes in **blue** if they show letters missed out.

<u>Underline</u> them in **red** if they show belonging. Some have both.

1. He isn't here.
2. Simon's shorts are muddy.
3. Where's the picture? It's on the wall.
4. The trees' leaves are beginning to fall.
5. He wouldn't go on Space Mountain.
6. The Great Wall of China's steep.
7. Where's the rabbit's cage?
8. The photocopier isn't working.
9. The yacht's cabin was small.
10. Is that Chris's bicycle? No. It's not.

Answer pages

N.B. Capital letters for 'mum' and 'dad' are optional but lower case is used in this book.

Page 3
1. When I try to sharpen a pencil, the lead always breaks. 2. He jumped over the box, climbed the wall bars and reached the top. 3. She typed the letter, signed it but forgot to post it. 4. I like to get up early, have breakfast and then brush my teeth. 5. I went to Los Angeles, San Francisco and San Diego. 6. If you go to the sales early, you should find some bargains. 7. Tomorrow, instead of having lessons, we are going on a school trip. 8. Whenever it rains, I forget my umbrella. 9. My sister, who is ten, will run in a marathon race. 10. The ducklings, although very small, could swim.

Page 4 (top)
1. I went to the shops and bought apples, oranges and grapes. 2. We took the car to have the tyres, the water and the oil checked. 3. My house has a lounge, kitchen, bathroom and two bedrooms. 4. You can skip, hop or jump. 5. Do not forget your ruler, pencil, rubber or pen. 6. I can run quickly, slowly, sideways or backwards.

Page 4 (bottom)
1. Gemma is a pretty, intelligent girl. 2. My uncle, George and Ayesha came to meet me. 3. I saw Philip, Martin and Nathan at the party.

Page 5 (top)
1. I saw the two large dogs, Bouncer and George, chasing the cat. 2. Miss Jones, one of my teachers, has a loud voice. 3. Beethoven, one of the greatest composers, was born in Germany. 4. Mr Edwards, our next door neighbour, has three pet rats. 5. The famous painting, the Mona Lisa, is very beautiful. 6. The film about an otter, Ring of Bright Water, is very sad.

Page 5 (bottom)
1. We went to hear a group play, Susan. 2. Did you know Patrick, Jean? 3. I went to feed Bilbo, the sea lion, Liam.

Page 6
1. Janice, a tall, pretty girl, won the race. 2. The River Trent, a large river in England, is very wide in parts. 3. The clown, a funny, fat man, had a white face and a red nose. 4. The match, watched by twenty thousand people, took place at Wembley. 5. Julius Caesar, a powerful Roman leader, conquered England. 6. The prince, a young and handsome man, married a duchess. 7. The lion, a bold and proud animal, is known as the king of beasts. 8. The cave, being so deep and narrow, was dangerous for potholers. 9. The bride's dress, handmade of pure silk, looked lovely. 10. The apple tree, although very old, always has juicy apples. 11. A Christmas Carol, a famous book by Charles Dickens, has been made into a film.

Page 7
1. The walk, so I am told, takes two hours. 2. The bus, by the way, is always late. 3. Australia, as we all know, was discovered by Captain Cook. 4. The lions in the park can, I believe, be very dangerous. 5. You will, of course, win a prize. 6. Saturday, I always feel, is a good day for shopping. 7. Whatever happens, do not cross the road until it is safe. 8. I am sure that, no matter how long it takes, she will finish it. 9. She is a good cook, I think, but she uses too much salt. 10. The Hobbit, although very long, is an exciting book. 11. Zahid, in spite of my warning, jumped into the pool.

Page 8
1. I shall, if I save my pocket money, be able to go shopping with my friend. 2. The man, who was very strong, carried the huge rock. 3. We climbed the hill, even though we were tired, and reached the top. 4. The butterfly, so colourful and small, landed on the flower. 5. She, like her father, is good at sport. 6. The squirrel, having collected the acorns, ran up the tree. 7. An American athlete, who ran very fast, won the race. 8. The clock, which belonged to my aunt, keeps good time. 9. The dog, who was called Charlie, chased the ball. 10. The water, though cold, was very refreshing. 11. The red shoes, which fitted well, matched my new dress.

Page 9 (top)
1. The mountain bicycle, which I bought from my friend, works very well. 2. I took my trainers, racquet, track suit and towel with me. 3. Her hat, covered in feathers, stopped me from seeing the screen. 4. Ann, Hazel, Catherine and Jane are in our group. 5. The maple tree, with the sun shining on its red leaves, is very pretty. 6. If you go the wrong way, you will end up in a field. 7. Mr. Benson, the old caretaker, works very hard. 8. In our garden there are roses, daffodils, tulips and pansies. 9. The artist, who is my uncle, sketches very well. 10 I shall, I hope, dive off the top board today.

Page 10 (top) *Some exclamation marks are optional*
1. Beware! 2. I've won first prize! 3. I'm drowning! Help! 4. Come quickly! The house is on fire! 5. Be quiet! Dad is listening to the football results. 6. Goodness! He's coming back in five minutes. 7. What a dreadful film! Shall we go home and watch a video? 8. Don't panic! They've put out the fire.

Page 10 (bottom)
1. Sit still! I'm trying to cut your toenails. 2. Listen! Can you hear the thunder? 3. Have you seen the Loch Ness Monster? Of course not! 4. Quick! The bus is leaving. 5. Can you go to camp? Gosh! No. 6. It is very late. Why are you still awake? 7. Goodness! Have you seen the state of the carpet? 8. Quick! The cat's been sick.

Answer pages (contd.)

Page 11 ~ only the lines which contain ! marks are shown (some are optional). All the others have full stops only.
1. My watch is wrong. I'm late! 2. The Queen has arrived. Stand up! 3. Please help! My hamster has escaped! 4. Stop! The traffic light is red. 5. Take this tray quickly! It's too heavy. 6. Move! The ladder is falling! 7. Watch out! The boat is sinking! 8. Wait! My foot is bleeding! 9. We will never get tickets. Just look at the queue!

Page 12 (bottom)
He has - he's **OR** He hasn't   Here is - here's   Could not - couldn't

Page 13 (bottom)
1. he'll 2. I'll 3. He'll 4. We've 5. they've 6. It'll 7. you'll 8. who've 9. you've

Page 14
1. Hurry up! They're coming soon. 2. We knew that we were right and he was wrong. 3. He says we're early but we're not. 4. I think you're good at sport. 5. She was looking forward to her piano lesson. 6. He's moving to a new house. 7. They're very good value for money. 8. We look alike because we're sisters. 9. We were going shopping to buy some books.

Page 15 (top)
1. He said that they'd never agree. 2. You'd be frightened if you stepped on a snake. 3. They told us that we'd be able to sit at the front. 4. She said that she'd go to see the film. 5. It shouldn't be dangerous and it'll be fun. 6. My dad couldn't go until six o'clo

Page 15 (bottom)
1. She won't go in the attic because she's seen a mouse there.   2. They won't go near because of the alligators in the lake.

Page 16 (top)
1. The school had its Christmas party yesterday. 2. I think it's time to play tennis. 3. The monkey sat in its own dinner. 4. I hop it's not too busy. 5. Isa says that it's always hot in India. 6. The Air Force flew its first jet plane.

Page 16 (bottom)
1. The tiger chased its prey. 2. I think it's going to snow. 3. The adder is dangerous; its venom is poisonous. 4. The newspaper changed its name. 5. They say that it's hard to skate. 6. I think that it's fun to go to Stoke Park.

Page 17 (top)
2. He's going to Africa. 3. She hasn't had her hair cut. 4. What's on the television? 5. It's a good book. 6. He doesn't mind. 7. Where's my bag? 8. We're not going to the fair. 9. She's a teacher. 10. That's a good idea.

Page 17 (bottom)
1. My friend is sad. He has lost his pen. 2. The hat is too big. 3. He has not chosen me to play in the team. 4. They are not happ to go if it is busy. 5. Who is going to see if he is all right? 6. We are not sure if he has won the cup. 7. Where is the mouse? The cage is empty.

Page 18 (top)
1. the horse's head 2. the shark's fin 3. the cat's owner 4. the lorry's tyres 5. the baby's rattle 6. William's uncle 7. my dad' job 8. the team's mascot 9. Jenny's bag 10. the swimming pool's edge 11. the girl's dress 12. the rat's tail 13. the dog's dinn 14. the boy's cricket bat

Page 18 (bottom)
1. The tap's washer was worn.   2. It is Jane's birthday next week.   3. Do you know if that is Stephen's photograph? 4. Can you find your mother's purse?   5. Ranjit's bike is very smart.   2. I hope the dog's bark will not wake the neighbour's baby.

Page 19
2. the cat's kittens 3. my teacher's pen 4. the girl's purse 5. the apple's core 6. the runner's shoe 7. the giraffe's neck 8. the teapot's lid 9. my uncle's brother 10. the milkman's van 11. the knight's sword 12. the deer's antler 13. the pencil's le 14. the skirt's hem 15. Queen Mary's throne 16. the school's main exit 17. the cow's tail 18. the boy's ruler 19. Paul's friend 20. the lake's depth

Page 20
2. Phyllis's husband is David. 3. Marcus's sister is Mavis. 4. Tom's daughter is Iris. 5. Adam's grandmother is Phyllis. 6. Morris's father is John. 7. Jess's daughter is Beth. 8. Simon's mother is Jess. 9. David's granddaughters are Iris and Beth.

Page 21 (top)
Examples to be <u>underlined</u>: 1. That chair's leg is broken. 2. This is Mark's scarf. 3. Where is the dog's lead? 4. That is Joan's favourite song. 5. Anisa is Hassan's sister.

Page 21
1. That is Jean's bicycle. 2. Oxfam needs lots of blankets, warm clothes and jumpers. 3. The postman's bag was full of letters. 4. There were books and toys for sale at the bazaar. 5. James's video tape was brilliant. 6. Peter's watch was being mended so he used Ross's. 7. The play's ending was very good. 8. Mum's scales were broken so she used my sister's scales. 9. We used sticky tape to hold the pages together. 10. She met me at my uncle's house.

Answer pages (contd.)

Page 22 (top)
1. pl 2. sing 3. pl 4. pl 5. sing

Page 22 (bottom)
1. The butcher's shop is closed. 2. That is next year's calendar. 3. There are birds' nests in the beech trees. 4. Sandra dropped the speckled hen's egg. 5. This ship's sails are red. 6. My ski's clip is broken. 7. Shahab's pencils were blunt. 8. The cricket team's score was high. 9. Those are Emily's shoes.

Page 23 (top)
1. Policemen's wives can be very lonely. 2. The women's changing rooms are cold. 3. He was a wolf in sheep's clothing. 4. The men's room is on the top floor. 5. It is difficult to see trout's eyes. 6. Children's shoes are very expensive. 7. People's wishes must be carried out.

Page 23 (bottom)
1. Sheep's wool often clings to fences. 2. The style of women's shoes is always changing. 3. Postmen's bicycles are often red. 4. The children's teacher always has an apple for lunch.

Page 24 (top)
1. William's coat is too big. 2. Both the teams' captains were popular. 3. The firemen's hoses were tangled. 4. Somebody's watch has a loud alarm. 5. It was Nigel's fault. 6. Raj's bicycle has six gears. 7. It is hard to find bears' dens. 8. I clung to the horse's mane.
9. I can't remember the song's name. 10. All the chains' links were strong and held the ship's anchor firmly.

Page 24 (bottom)
1. Harry's parrot is very clever. 2. I saw Luke's team win. 3. I nearly fell over the cliff's edge. 4. Jack's brother is good at maths.
5. The thieves' car broke down. 6. I went to the ladies' hairdresser. 7. That ruler's numbers are hard to see. 8. Aeroplanes' cargoes are kept in the hold.

Page 26 (top)
1. Where's my drink? 2. It's hard to understand. 3. I can't think straight. 4. I haven't cleaned my teeth. 5. We aren't lucky.
6. David's gone home.

Page 26 (middle)
1. The nurse's uniform was white. 2. Flamingoes' legs are very thin. 3. The conjuror's trick was very clever. 4. Kate's photograph made us laugh. 5. The two boys' diving belts were heavy.

Page 26 (bottom)
1. letters missed out 2. 'belonging' apostrophe 3. letters missed out 4. 'belonging' apostrophe 5. letters missed out.
6. letters missed out 7. letters missed out & 'belonging' apostrophe 8. letters missed out 9. 'belonging' apostrophe
10. 'belonging' apostrophe & letters missed out